This Book Belongs to

...... Sophia ....

.... Lilly ....

....

Age ....

©1991 Grandreams Limited.
This edition printed in 1997.

Illustrated by Pam Storey.

Published by
Grandreams Limited
435-437 Edgware Road, Little Venice
London W2 1TH

Printed in Hong Kong.

Bye, Baby Bunting

Hush Little Baby

Twinkle, Twinkle, Little Star

Rock-A-Bye, Baby

**And Other
Bedtime Lullabies**

Bye baby bunting,
Daddy's gone a-hunting,
Off to get a rabbit skin,
To wrap his baby bunting in.

Oh slumber my darling,
Thy sire is a knight,
Thy mother is a lady,
So lovely and bright.
The hills and the dales
From the towers which we see,
Shall one day belong,
My sweet infant to thee.
Oh, rest thee, Babe, rest thee babe
Sleep while you may.

I see the moon,
And the moon sees me;
God bless the moon,
And God bless me.

Hush-a-ba birdie, croon, croon,
Hush-a-birdie, croon,
The sheep are gane to the silver wood,
And the cows are gane to the broom, broom.

And it's braw milking the kye, kye,
It's braw milking the kye,
The birds are singing, the bells are ringing,
The wild deer come galloping by, by.

And hush-a-ba birdie, croon, croon,
Hush-a-birdie, croon,
The gaits are gane to the mountain hie,
And they'll no be hame till noon, noon.

The flowers have gone to beddy,
The moon has begun to shine,
Each nods its little headdy
Upon its stem so fine.
The branches rustle;
And they seem to sigh, as in a dream
Sleepy, sleepy, sleepy,
Sleep, my baby, sleep.

The birds that sing so sweetly by day,
Have gone to rest,
And each is tucked up neatly,
All in its little nest,
The cottage in the garden here
Is still awake, I fear.
Sleepy, sleepy, sleepy,
Sleep, my baby, sleep.

The sandman will be coming
And poking in his head,
To look for naughty children
That haven't gone to bed;
And if he takes them by surprise,
The sand flies in their eyes.
Sleepy, sleepy, sleepy,
Sleep, my baby, sleep.

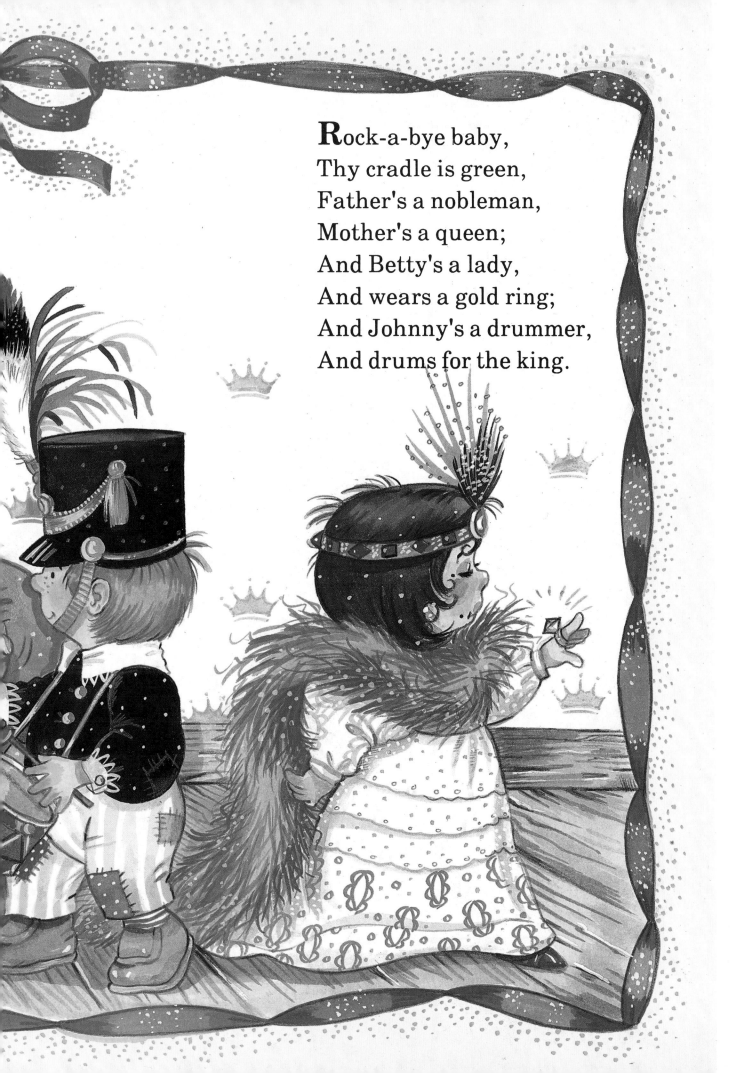

Rock-a-bye baby,
Thy cradle is green,
Father's a nobleman,
Mother's a queen;
And Betty's a lady,
And wears a gold ring;
And Johnny's a drummer,
And drums for the king.

Now I lay me down to sleep,
I pray the Lord my soul to keep;
And if I die before I wake,
I pray the Lord my soul to take.

God bless this house from thatch to floor,
The twelve apostles guard the door
Four angels to my bed;
Gabriel stands at the head,
John and Peter at my feet,
All to watch me while I sleep.

Oh, I wish I were a fairy,
With a pair of silver wings,
And a lot of shining stardust in my hair.
I would frolic with the butterflies,
And bees and flying things,
And I'd dine upon the daintiest of fare.
I would sup upon a dewdrop
And I'd sleep within a rose,
Only to be awakened by a droning bumblebee.
And if I should chance to tumble,
Off into another doze,
There would not be a single soul to see.

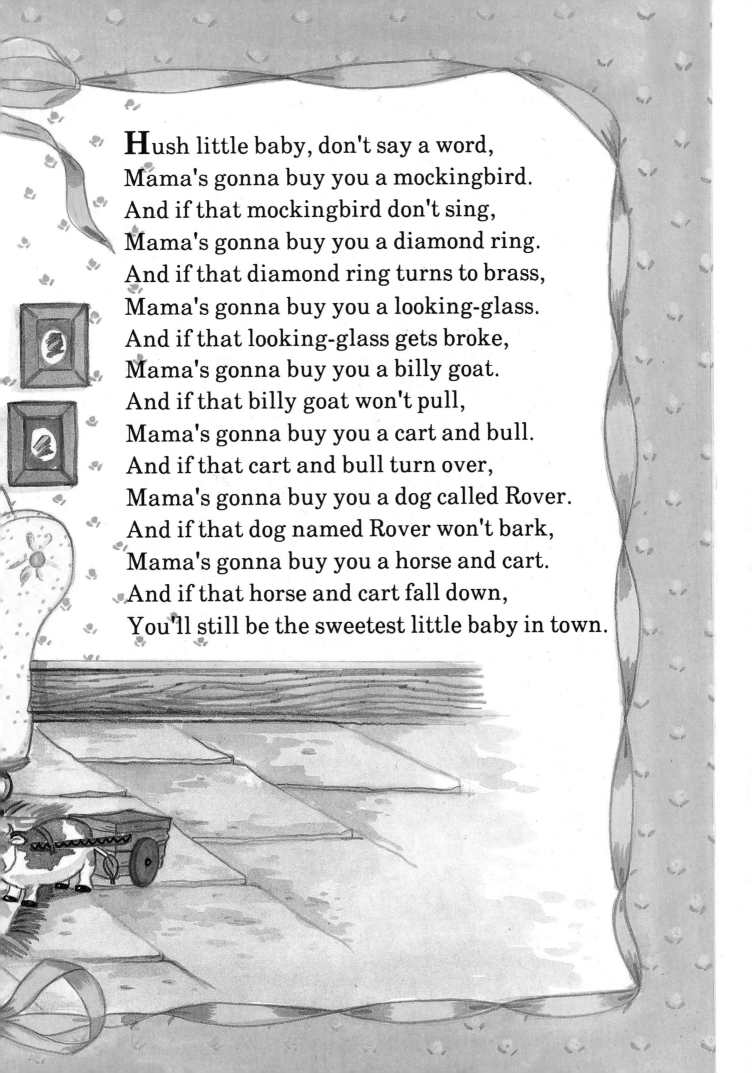

Hush little baby, don't say a word,
Mama's gonna buy you a mockingbird.
And if that mockingbird don't sing,
Mama's gonna buy you a diamond ring.
And if that diamond ring turns to brass,
Mama's gonna buy you a looking-glass.
And if that looking-glass gets broke,
Mama's gonna buy you a billy goat.
And if that billy goat won't pull,
Mama's gonna buy you a cart and bull.
And if that cart and bull turn over,
Mama's gonna buy you a dog called Rover.
And if that dog named Rover won't bark,
Mama's gonna buy you a horse and cart.
And if that horse and cart fall down,
You'll still be the sweetest little baby in town.

The sandman comes, the sandman comes,
With such pretty snow white sand,
For he is known throughout the land,
The sandman comes.

Star light, star bright,
First star I see tonight,
I wish I may, I wish I might,
Have the wish I wish tonight.

Baby, baby, naughty baby,
Hush you squalling thing, I say.
Peace this moment, peace or maybe
Bonaparte will pass this way.

Sweet and low, sweet and low,
Wind of the western sea;
Low, low, breathe and blow,
Wind of the western sea!
Over the rolling waters go,
Come from the dying moon and blow,
Blow him again to me,
While my little one,
While my pretty one,
Sleeps.
Sleep and rest, sleep and rest,
Father will come to thee soon,
Rest, rest, on mother's breast,
Father will come to thee soon.
Father will come to his babe in the nest,
Silver sails all out of the west,
Under the silver moon.
Sleep, my little one,
Sleep my pretty one,
Sleep.

Little man in coal pit
Goes knock, knock, knock;
Up he comes, up he comes,
Out at the top.

Go to bed first,
A golden purse;
Go to bed second,
A golden pheasant;
Go to bed third,
A golden bird.

Down with the lambs,
Up with the lark,
Run to bed children
Before it gets dark.

Hush thee, my babby,
Lie still with thy daddy,
Thy mammy has gone to the mill,
To grind thee some wheat
To make thee some meat,
So hush-a-bye, babby, lie still.

Twinkle, twinkle, little star -
How I wonder what you are!
Up above the world so high,
Like a diamond in the sky.
Twinkle, twinkle, little star -
How I wonder what you are!

Sleep baby sleep, and good night,
All the birds are asleep and out of sight,
Quiet the lambs on the hill,
Even the bumblebees are still.
Only the man in the moon
Is still nodding, but soon
Over him slumber will creep,
Sleep, baby, sleep, go to sleep.
Good night,
Good night.

Sleep, baby, sleep;
Thy father is watching the sheep,
Thy mother is shaking the dreamland tree,
And down falls a little dream on thee,
Sleep, baby, sleep,
Sleep, baby, sleep.

Sleep, baby, sleep;
The large stars are the sheep,
The little stars are the lambs, I guess,
And the bright moon is the shepherdess.
Sleep, baby, sleep,
Sleep, baby, sleep.

Hush-a-bye, baby, they're gone to milk,
Lady and milkmaid all in silk,
Lady goes softly, maid goes slow,
Round again, round again, round they go.

From breakfast on through all the day
At home among my friends I stay,
But every night I go abroad
Afar into the land of Nod.

All by myself I have to go,
With none to tell me what to do -
All alone beside the streams
And up the mountainsides of dreams.

The strangest things are there for me,
Both things to eat and things to see,
And many frightening sights abroad
Till morning in the land of Nod.

A linden tree is standing
Beside a running stream;
I lay beneath its shadows
And dreamed a happy dream.

The rustling of its branches
Was like a lullaby;
I listened to its stories,
As I watched the clouds go by.

Matthew, Mark, Luke and John,
Bless the bed that I lie on.
Four corners to my bed,
Four angels round my head;
One to watch and one to pray
And two to bear my soul away.

Good night, God bless you,
Go to bed and undress you
Good night , sweet repose.
Half the bed and all the clothes.

I'll buy you a tartan bonnet,
And feathers to put upon it,
With a hush-a-bye and a lullaby,
Because you are so like your daddy.

Rock-a-bye baby on the tree top,
When the wind blows the cradle will rock,
When the bough breaks the cradle will fall,
And down will come baby, cradle and all.

Lullaby and good night,
With roses bedight
With lilies bedecked
Is baby's wee bed;
Lay thee down now and rest,
May thy slumber be blessed.
Lay thee down now and rest,
May thy slumber be blessed.

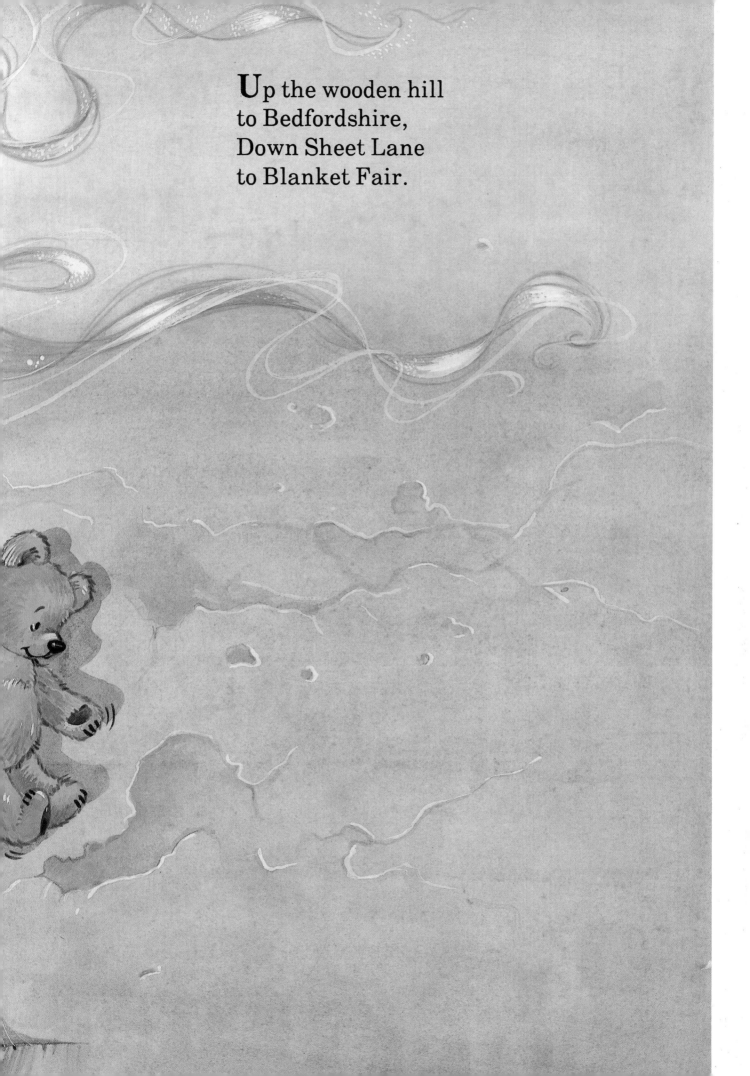

Up the wooden hill
to Bedfordshire,
Down Sheet Lane
to Blanket Fair.

Hush-a-baa baby,
Dinna mak' a din,
An' ye'll get a cakie
When the baker comes in.

The evening is coming, the sun sinks to rest,
The crows are all flying straight home to their nests.
"Caw," says the crow as he flies over head,
It's time little people were going to bed.

The flowers are dozing,
The daisies asleep.
The primroses are buried in slumber so deep.
Closed for the night are the roses so red,
It's time little people were going to bed.

How many miles to babyland?
Anyone can tell;
Up one flight and to your right;
Don't forget to ring the bell.

What do they do in babyland?
They dream and wake and play;
They laugh and crow, and fonder grow.
Jolly times have they.

Diddle, diddle, dumpling, my son John,
Went to bed with his trousers on;
One shoe off, and one shoe on,
Diddle, diddle, dumpling, my son John.

Go to bed, Tom,
Go to bed, Tom,
Tired or not, Tom,
Go to bed, Tom.

The little lady lairdie
She longed for a baby-o,
She took her father's greyhound
And rowed it in a plaidie-o,
Saying, Hishie, Bishie, bow, wow,
Long legs hast thou,
If it wasn't for your cold nose
I would kiss thee now-o.